S0-BYO-390

Supplement to

THE ECONOMIC ANALYSIS OF CAPITAL EXPENDITURES FOR MANAGERS AND ENGINEERS

G.T. Stevens, Jr.

Pearson
Custom
Publishing

Copyright © 2000 by Pearson Custom Publishing.
All rights reserved.

Permission in writing must be obtained from the publisher before any part of this work may be reproduced or transmitted in any form or by any means, electronic or mechanical, including photocopying and recording, or by any information storage or retrieval system.

Printed in the United States of America

10 9 8 7 6 5

This manuscript was supplied camera-ready by the author(s).

Please visit our web site at www.pearsoncustom.com

ISBN 0–536–60460-6

BA 990858

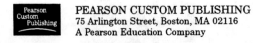

PEARSON CUSTOM PUBLISHING
75 Arlington Street, Boston, MA 02116
A Pearson Education Company

CONTENTS

CHAPTER 1

INTRODUCTION

This book is a supplement to the text <u>The Economic Analysis of Capital Expenditures for Managers and Engineers</u> written by G. T. Stevens, Jr. and published by Ginn Press (1994). Since its publication, Ginn Press is now Pearson Custom Publishing.

The purpose of this supplement is to provide additional topics, expansion of topics, and additional problems. Also, the chapter on taxes (Chapter 4) has been revised to reflect recent changes in various tax rates.

This supplement follows the same chapter sequence as the original text. A summary of the additions follows:

Chapter 2

1. Mid-point cash flows

2. Geometric sequences of cash flows

3. Additional problems

Chapter 3

1. Depreciation amounts using the half-year conversion

2. Additional problems

Chapter 4

1. New tax rates on corporate income

2. Basis of MACRS percentages

3. Additional problems

Chapter 12

1. A mathematical basis is presented for determining MARR for new projects

2. Additional problems

Chapters 13, 14, & 15

No new material is presented

Listed below are some corrections that should be made to the text.

Page 74

Problem 3-17: change the word "estimated" to actual.

Page 126 (Table 5-10)

The cash flow for year 4 is

$x_4 = (4,000,000 - 402,800) - (4,000,000 - 402,800 - 612,000)(.4) - 556,000$

$= \$1,847,120$

Page 137

Table 5-13 is

Table 5-13

Net Present Values for Example 5-6

i	NPV
0	50
10	13
20	0
30	-3
50	0
70	3
100	0

The value $36,204 should be $36,024.

CHAPTER 2

INTEREST AND INTEREST FACTORS

In this chapter two additional interest factors are presented. They are (1) mid-point cash flows and (2) geometric sequences of cash flows.

MID-POINT FLOWS

The equal amounts (A) used in the text occur at the end of a period, another possibility is for the equal amounts to occur at the mid-points of a period as shown in Figure S2-1.

- - - - - - - - - - - - - - - - - - -

Figure S2-1 Here

- - - - - - - - - - - - - - - - - - -

The future accumulated amount, F, shown in Figure S2-1 can be determined using the usual F/A factor if A^1 is converted to an equivalent end of the year amount, A. Using a yearly compounded rate, i, the conversion of A^1 is determined by

$$A = A^1 \left(F \Big/ P \frac{r}{2}, 1 \right) \tag{S2-1}$$

where $\frac{r}{2}$ is an effective semi-annual rate. Since i is a yearly rate $\frac{r}{2}$ is

$$i = \left(1 + \frac{r}{2} \right)^2 - 1 \tag{S2-2}$$

$$\frac{r}{2} = (1+i)^{\frac{1}{2}} - 1 \tag{S2-3}$$

Now,

$$F \Big/ P \frac{r}{2}, 1 = \left(1 + \frac{r}{2} \right) \tag{S2-4}$$

FIGURE S2-1

Mid-Point Cash Flows

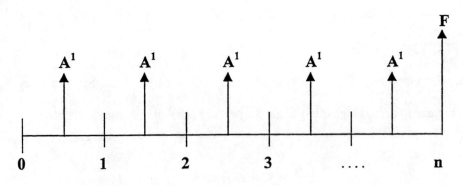

End of Years

And substituting Eq. (S2-3) into Eq. (S2-4) gives

$$F/P\frac{r}{2}, 1 = \left(1 + (1+i)^{\frac{1}{2}} - 1\right) \qquad \text{(S2-5)}$$

and, therefore,

$$F/P\frac{r}{2}, 1 = (1+i)^{\frac{1}{2}} \qquad \text{(S2-6)}$$

substituting Eq. (S2-6) into Eq. (S2-1) gives

$$A = A^{1}(1+i)^{\frac{1}{2}} \qquad \text{(S2-7)}$$

and the accumulated amount of the end of n years is

$$F = A^{1}(1+i)^{\frac{1}{2}} F/A\,i\,, n \qquad \text{(S2-8)}$$

In effect, the term $(1+i)^{\frac{1}{2}}$ is a conversion factor. When other factors are involved, the conversion factor is used as shown in the following equations:

$$P = A^{1}\left((1+i)^{\frac{1}{2}} PAi, n\right) \qquad \text{(S2-9)}$$

$$A^{1} = \frac{P(A/Pi, n)}{(1+i)^{\frac{1}{2}}} \qquad \text{(S2-10)}$$

$$A^{1} = \frac{F(A/Fi, n)}{(1+i)^{\frac{1}{2}}} \qquad \text{(S2-11)}$$

Example S2-1_____

An equal amount of $1,000 is deposited into an account at the mid-point of each year for a period of six years. Determine the accumulated amount if

(a) the interest rate is 10% compounded yearly.

(b) the interest rate is 10% compounded semi-annually.

(c)   the interest rate is 10% compounded quarterly.

The answer to part (a) using Eq. (S2-8) is

$$F = 1,000(1 + .10)^{\frac{1}{2}} \text{ (F/A 10,6)}$$

$$= 1,000 \ (1.0488)(7.716)$$

$$= \$8,092.54$$

For Part (b), the effective semi-annual rate is

$$\frac{r}{2} = \frac{.10}{2} = .05 = 5\%$$

and the effective annual rate (Eq. (2-31) in the text)

$$\left(1+\frac{.10}{2}\right)^{2} - 1 = .1025 = 10.25\%$$

Therefore,

$$A = 1,000 \text{ F/P } 5,1 = 1,050$$

and

$$F = 1,050 \text{ F/A } 10.25, 6$$

$$= 1,050 \ (7.764)$$

$$= \$8,152.20$$

For Part (c), the effective annual rate is

$$\left(1+\frac{.10}{4}\right)^{4} - 1 = .1038 = 10.38\%$$

and

$$F = 1,000(1.1038)^{\frac{1}{2}} \text{ F/A } 10.38,6$$

$$= 1,000 \ (1.0506)(7.790)$$

$$= \$8,184.17$$

GEOMETRIC SEQUENCES

Cash flow sequences can be increasing or decreasing at a constant rate. In these cases, a composite rate can be defined that allows the calculation of the present or future amounts.

An Increasing Sequence: An increasing sequence is shown in Figure S2-12, where g is

- - - - - - - - - - - - - - - - - - -

Figure S2-2 Here

- - - - - - - - - - - - - - - - - - -

the constant rate. It should be noted that the first amount occurs at time zero. The present value of the cash flows in Figure S2-2 is

$$P = A_0 + A_0 (1 + g)(1 + i)^{-1} + A_0 (1 + g)^2(1 + i)^{-2} + ...$$
$$+ A_0 (1 + g)^i(1 + i)^{-j} + ... + A_0 (1 + g)^n(1 + i)^{-n} \quad (S2\text{-}12)$$

or

$$P = A_0 + A_0 \sum_{j=1}^{n}\left(\frac{1+g}{1+i}\right)^{j} \quad (S2\text{-}13)$$

A composite rate, i_c, can be defined for the increasing sequence as

$$i_c = \frac{1+i}{1+g} - 1 \quad (S2\text{-}14)$$

and rearranging, Eq. (S2-14) gives

$$\frac{1+g}{1+i} = \frac{1}{1+i_c} \quad (S2\text{-}15)$$

Substituting Eq. S2-15 into Eq. S2-13 gives

$$P = A_0 + A_0 \sum_{j=1}^{n}\left(\frac{1}{1+i_c}\right)^{j} \quad (S2\text{-}16)$$

FIGURE S2-2

A Geometric Sequence of
Cash Flows

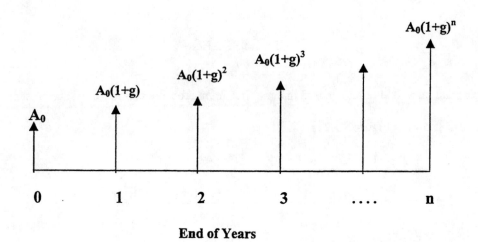

Since the P/A factor is the summation of the P/F factors, Eq. S2-16 can be written as

$$P = A_0 + A_0 \; P/Ai_c, \, n \qquad\qquad (S2\text{-}17)$$

EXAMPLE S2-2_____

A geometric sequence of cash flows is increasing at a rate of 5%, the first cash flow, which occurs now, (A_0), is $1,000. What is the present value of this sequence for a period of four years.

Using Eq. (S2-14), the composite rate is

$$\frac{1+.10}{1+.06} = 0.03774 = 3.774\%$$

and using Eq. (S2-17), the present value is

$$P \;=\; 1,000 + 1,000 \; PA \; 3.774, \, 4$$

$$=\; 1,000 + 1,000 \; (3.6493)$$

$$=\; \$4,649.30$$

As a check of the answer, Eq. (S2-12) is used

$$P = 1,000 + 1,000 \; \{(1.06)(1.10)^{-1} + (1.06)^2(1.10)^2$$

$$+ \, (1.06)^3(1.10)^{-3} + (1.06)^4(1.06)^{-4} \; \}$$

$$= 1,000 + 1,000 \; \{.9636 + .9286 + .8948 + .8622\}$$

$$= 1,000 + 1,000 \; \{3.648.9\}$$

$$= \$4,648.90$$

The difference is due to round-off error.

Suppose in this example, the values of "g" and "i" are reversed. Now the composite rate is

$$i_c = \frac{1+.06}{1+.10} - 1 = -0.03636 = -3.636\%$$

Although i_c is negative, Eq. (S2-17) is still applicable.

$$PA - 3.636,4 = \frac{(1-.03636)^4 - 1}{(-.03636)(1-.03636)^4}$$

$$= \frac{.8623 - 1}{-.03135}$$

$$= \frac{-.1377}{-.03135}$$

$$= 4.3919$$

and Eq. (S2-17) gives

$$P = 1,000 + 1,000 \, (4.3917)$$

$$= \$5,391.70$$

As some extensions to Example S2-2, the equivalent equal annual amount beginning at the end of year one is given by

$$A = P(A/P \; i,n) \tag{S2-18}$$

and the accumulated amount at the end of the sequence is

$$F = P(F/Pi, \, n) \tag{S2-19}$$

Another Sequence: Eq. (S2-17) is based on the first cash flow occurring at $j = 0$ with the growth rate, g, also beginning at this point in time. Another sequence is possible as shown in Figure S2-3. Here the first cash flow occurs at the end of the first year and the growth begins the second year.

- - - - - - - - - - - - - - - - - - -

See Figure S2-3 on next page

- - - - - - - - - - - - - - - - - - -

In this situation Eq. (S2-13) becomes.

$$P = A_1 \sum_{j=1}^{n} \frac{(1+g)^{j-1}}{(1+j)^{j}} \qquad \text{(S2-20)}$$

Multiplying Eq. (S2-20) by $\left(\dfrac{1+g}{1+g}\right)$ gives

$$P = \frac{A_1}{(1+g)} \sum_{j=1}^{n} \left(\frac{1+g}{1+j}\right)^{j} \qquad \text{(S2-21)}$$

and using the composite rate, Eq. (S2-21) becomes

$$P = \frac{A_1}{1+g} \, PA \, i_c, n \qquad \text{(S2-22)}$$

<u>A Decreasing Geometric Sequence:</u> The present value of a decreasing geometric sequence can be determined by defining a different composite rate than that used with an increasing sequence. For the sequence shown in Figure S2-4, the present value is

- - - - - - - - - - - - - - - - - - -

Figure S2-4 Here

- - - - - - - - - - - - - - - - - - -

$$P = A_0 + A_0 (1+g)^{-1}(1+i)^{-1} + A_0 (1+g)^{-2}(1+i)^{-2}$$

$$+ \ldots + A_0 (1+g)^{-j} (1+i)^{-j}$$

$$+ \ldots + A_0 (1+g)^{-n}(1+i)^{-n} \qquad \text{(S2-23)}$$

FIGURE S2-3

A Geometric Sequence of Cash Flows
Starting at j = 1

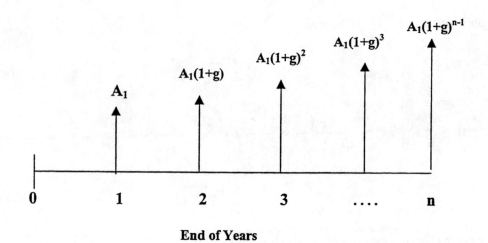

End of Years

FIGURE S2-4

A Decreasing Geometric Series
With the First Cash Flow at $j = 0$

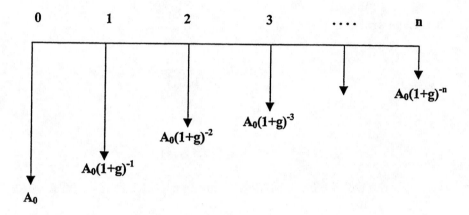

or

$$P = A_0 + A_0 \sum_{j=1}^{n} \frac{1}{(1+g)^j (1+i)^j} \tag{S2-24}$$

Defining a composite rate for the decreasing sequence, i_d, as

$$i_d = i + g + (i)(g) \tag{S2-25}$$

Eq. (S2-24) can be written as

$$P = A_0 + A_0 \sum_{j=1}^{n} \frac{1}{(1+i_d)^j} \tag{S2-26}$$

or

$$P = A_0 + A_0 \left(P/A\, i_d, n \right) \tag{S2-27}$$

For a decreasing series with the first cash flow occurring at j = 1, as shown in Figure S2-5, the

----

Figure S2-5 Here

----

present value is

$$P = A_1 \sum \frac{1}{(1+g)^{j-1} (1+i)^j} \tag{S2-28}$$

Multiplying this equation by $\left(\dfrac{1+g}{1+g} \right)$ gives

$$P = A_1 (1+g) \sum \frac{1}{(1+g)^j (1+i)^j} \tag{S2-29}$$

which can be written as

$$P = A_1 (1+g)\, PA\, i_d, n \tag{S2-30}$$

FIGURE S2-5

A Decreasing Geometric Sequence
With the First Cash Flow at $j = 1$

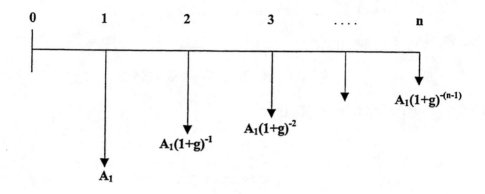

EXAMPLE S2-3_____

A geometric sequence of cash flows is decreasing at a rate of 6%. What is the present value of these cash flows for four years if i = 10% and

(a) the first cash flow occurs at j = 0 and is $1,000

(b) the first cash flow occurs at j = 1 and is $1,000

Since this is a decreasing series, the composite rate, using Eq. (S2-25)

$$i_d = .10 + .06 + (.1)(.06) = .166 = 16.6\%$$

and the answer for Part (a) using Eq. (S2-27) is

$$P = 1,000 + 1,000 \ P/A \ 16.6, 4$$

$$= 1,000 + 1,000 \ (2.765)$$

$$= \$3,765$$

For Part (b), using Eq. (S2-30), the answer is

$$P = 1,000 \ (1 + .06) \ PA \ 16.6, 4$$

$$= 1,000 \ (1.06)(2.765)$$

$$= \$2,931$$

_____

PROBLEMS

S2-1. A company believes its annual gross sales at the end of the first year will be $5(10)^6$ and increase by $0.4(10)^6$ every year for the next five years. Thereafter, it will decrease by $200,000 every year for the next five years. If the interest rate is 8%, determine an equivalent annual amount of gross sales over the ten-year period.

S2-2. A company plans to issue a $1,000 bond that will mature in ten years. It plans to sell this bond for $950. The interest rate being required by the bond market is 12%. What contractual rate should be put on the bond in order that it can be sold for $950?

S2-3. A person has the following two outstanding debts:

1. $5,000 borrowed at 10% compounded yearly to be paid back monthly over a period of five years. A payment has just been made and there are 36 remaining payments.

2. $3,000 borrowed at 8% compounded yearly to be paid monthly over two years. A payment has just been made and there are ten payments remaining. A friendly finance company agrees to pay off the debts for a monthly payment of $106.81 paid over five years. Determine,

    (a) the interest rate the finance company is charging

    (b) the additional interest being paid on the finance company's offer.

S2-4. A person plans to retire in twenty years. He wants to receive $15,000 per quarter starting three months after retirement for a period of ten-years. He believes his retirement fund will pay 4% compounded yearly. In order to provide for this retirement, what monthly payment must be deposited into an account that pays 6%, compounded annually?

S2-5. If a person deposits $2,000 a year at the mid-point of each year, determine the accumulated amount after ten years if

    (a)   the interest rate is 8% compounded yearly

    (b)   the interest rate is 8% compounded semiannually

    (c)   the interest rate is 8% compounded monthly.

S2-6. What is the equal annual mid-point value for a present amount of $10,000 over eight

years if the interest rate is

(a)   12% compounded yearly

(b)   12% compounded semiannually

(c)   12% compounded quarterly

S2-7. A geometric yearly cash flow series that starts now ($j = 0$) increases at a rate of 3%. If

the interest rate is 8%, determine the present value for a period of six years with an initial

amount of $2,000.

S2-8. What is the future accumulated amount for Problem S2-7?

S2-9. Repeat Problem S2-7 with an increasing rate of 6% and an interest rate of 4%.

S2-10. Repeat Problem S2-7 only the first cash flow ($2,000) occurs at the end of the first year.

CHAPTER 3

DEPRECIATION

The discussion of depreciation models given in the text is straight-forward and no new models are presented in this supplement. However, a suggestion and an expansion is presented.

A SUGGESTION

It is suggested that it be noted that Eq. (3-18) given in the text for capital recovery and return gives the same result as Eq. (S3-1).

$$P(A/Pi,n) - L(A/Fi,n) \tag{S3-1}$$

The fact that they give the same result is obvious. However for some, this is not readily apparent. In some review manuals for the Engineers-In-Training (EIT) examination, Eq. (S3-1) is used.

SOME DEPRECIATION CALCULATIONS

Questions often arise on the calculation of the depreciation amounts given in Table 4-10 of the text because of the half-year convention used. The method of calculating these is shown in the following discussion. First since SYD with a five-year depreciation period is used, the sum of the digits is $\frac{5(6)}{2} = 15$. Since only a half year's depreciation is taken in year one, the depreciation is

$$D_1 = \frac{5}{15}\left(\frac{1}{2}\right)(12,000) = \$2,000$$

Because of this half-year depreciation, there is in actuality six years of depreciation. the remaining depreciation amounts are

$$D_2 = \frac{4.5}{15}(12,000) = \$3,600$$

$$D_3 = \frac{3.5}{15}(12,000) = \$2,800$$

$$D_4 = \frac{2.5}{15}(12,000) = \$2,000$$

$$D_5 = \frac{1.5}{15}(12,000) = \$1,200$$

$$D_6 = \frac{0.5}{15}(12,000) = \$400$$

The use of the half-year convention is also used in determining the depreciation percentages used in the MACRS tax depreciation percentages (Chapter 4 of the text). An example of determining these percentages is given in Chapter 4 of this supplement.

PROBLEMS_____

S3-1. Show, numerically, that Eq. (S3-1) and the text Eq. (3-18) give the same result using the following data:

    First cost = $10,000

    Salvage = $1,000

    Depreciation period = 10 years

    Return = 8%

S3-2. Determine the depreciation schedule using the half-year convention with SYD, a depreciation period of 8 years, an initial cost of $100,000 and a salvage of $10,000.

S3-3. Determine the depreciation schedule using DDB depreciation with a switch to straight-line for an asset with an initial cost of $100,000, a salvage of zero, and a period of eight years.

S3-4. Determine the equivalent annual amount of capital and recovery for an asset with an

initial cost of $150,000, a salvage of $20,000, a life of twelve years, and a return of 10%

using

     (a)   straight-line depreciation

     (b)   SYD depreciation

     (c)   DDB depreciation

     (Hint: Work smart, not hard)

S3-5. Determine the depreciation schedule using a switch to straight-line depreciation and the

half-year convention for an asset with an initial cost of $90,000, a zero salvage, and a

depreciation life of six years.

CHAPTER 4

SOME TAX CONSIDERATIONS

Since publishing the original text, there have been some changes to the tax regulations for corporations. The changes that relate to the topics are provided in this chapter.

INCOME TAXES

Additional tax brackets have been established and are shown in Table S4-1.

Table S4-1 Here

The basic effect of these tax brackets is to increase the maximum corporate rate from 34% to 35%. For example, the taxes on a taxable income of $20,000,000 are

$$T = (20,000,000 - 18,333,333)(.35) + 6,416,667$$

$$= \$7,000,000.$$

or

$$T = (20,000,000)(.35) = \$7,000,000$$

For taxable incomes above $335,000, the tax rate varies between 34% and 35%.

In the analysis of capital expenditures, a tax rate greater than 35% is often used. This is to approximate other taxes (state and local) and to offset possible future increases in tax rates. It is not usual to see tax rates of 40% to 45% used in economic studies.

CAPITAL GAINS AND LOSSES

This section in the text is essentially correct except for the following two changes.

1.   Long-term is defined as more than 18 months.

2.   The tax rates for corporations on long-term gains are a maximum of 35%.

TABLE S4-1

CORPORATE INCOME TAX RATES (1997)

| Taxable Income | | % On | Of the Amount |
Over	But not over	Pay + Excess	Over ----
0	50,000	0	15	0
50,000	75,000	7,500	25	50,000
75,000	100,000	13,750	34	75,000
100,000	335,000	22,250	39	100,000
335,000	10,000,000	113,900	34	335,000
10,000,000	15,000,000	3,400,000	35	10,000,000
15,000,000	18,333,333	5,150,000	38	15,000,000
18,333,333		6,416,667	35	18,333,333

It should be noted that under current tax law, corporations do not receive the same benefits as individuals on long-term capital gains and losses. The remaining discussion in the text for this section is the same.

DISPOSAL OF DEPRECIABLE PROPERTY AND BUSINESS REAL ESTATE

The definitions of Sec. 1245 and 1250 Property given in the text are still applicable. Also, the basic tax treatment of these two type of tax property is the same. However, there are some changes in the rates. For Sec. 1245 Property the maximum tax rate is 35% (instead of 34%). this is equal to the maximum tax rate on ordinary income. However, with the additional increments for ordinary income, there is an advantage to including any Sec. 1231 gains resulting from the disposal of Sec. 1245 property as ordinary income in addition to the required inclusion of depreciation recapture as ordinary income.

Example S4-1_____

A company has a taxable income of $30,000,000. It purchased a Sec. 1245 asset seven years ago for $800,000 and its current tax book value is $500,000. Determine the total tax liability for selling prices of (a) $700,000, (b) $200,000 (c) $1,000,000.

For Part (a), the tax is

$$t = 30,000,000(.35) + (700,000 - 500,000)(.35)$$

$$= 10,500,000 + 70,000 = \$10,570,000.$$

The term (700,000 – 500,000) is the depreciation recapture referred to in the tax laws.

For Part (b), the tax is

$$t = 30,000,000(.35) + (200,000 - 500,000)(.35)$$

$$= 10,500,000 - 105,000 = \$10,395,000.$$

The (200,000 – 500,000) is a Sec. 1231 loss.

For Part (c), the tax is

$$t = 30,000,000(.35) + (800,000 - 500,000)(.35)$$

$$+ (1,000,000 - 800,000)(.35)$$

$$t = 10,500,000 + 300,000 (.35) + 200,000(.35)$$

$$t = \$10,682,000$$

Where the $300,000 is depreciation recapture the $200,000 is a Sec. 1231 gain.

In Example S4-1 the taxable income is above $18,333,333 and, consequently, the tax rate is 35%. However, if the tax increase is less than this amount, the gains would be taken as ordinary income since the overall tax rate would be less. this is shown in Example S4-2.

Example S4-2_____

A company's taxable income is $80,000 before the sale of any property. It sells a Sec. 1245 asset for $70,000 that originally cost $60,000 with a tax book value of $10,000. The depreciation recapture is

$$60,000 - 10,000 = \$50,000$$

and the Sec. 1231 gain is

$$70,000 - 60,000 = \$10,000$$

Including the Sec. 1231 gain as ordinary income, the taxable income is

$$80,000 + 50,000 + 10,000 = \$140,000$$

and the taxes are

$$t = (50,000)(.15) + (25,000)(.25) + 25,000(.34)$$

$$+ (140,000 - 100,000)(.39)$$

$$= \$37,850$$

The overall tax rate is

$$T = \frac{37,850}{140,000} = 27.04\%$$

The discussion in the text regarding Sec. 1250 Property is still applicable except the maximum rate is 35%.

TAX DEPRECIATION

The discussion in the text of tax depreciation (MACRS) is still applicable. the method for determining the percentage rates used in MACRS is shown in the following discussion for 5 years.

First, MACRS is based on DDB with a switch to straight-line and a half-year convention. therefore for the first five years, the constant percentage (a) is

$$a = \frac{2}{5} = .40$$

and the percentage depreciation for a full year would be

$$D_1 = a(1-a)^{n-1} = \frac{2}{5}\left(1-\frac{2}{5}\right)^0 = \frac{2}{5}.$$

However, since the first year's depreciation is only a half-year, the depreciation factor is

$$D_1 = \frac{1}{2}\left(\frac{2}{5}\right) = .20 = 20\%$$

and the book value at the end of the first year is

$$B_1 = 1 - .2 = .8$$

The percentage depreciation for the second year is

$$D_2 = \frac{2}{5}(.8)^1 = .32 = 32\%$$

and the book value at the end of year two is

$$B_2 = 1 - .2 - .32 = .48$$

The percentage depreciation for year three is

$$D_3 = \frac{2}{5}(.48) = .192 = 19.2\%$$

The book value and the end of the third year is

$$B_3 = 1 - .2 - .48 - .192 = .288.$$

At this point the switch to straight-line is made and the percentage deprecations for years 4 and 5

are

$$D_4 = D_5 = \frac{.288}{2.5} = .1152 = 11.52\% \ .$$

The book value and the end of year five is

$$B_5 = 1 - .2 - .48 - .192 - .1152 = .0576 \ .$$

Therefore, the depreciation factor for year 6 is

$$D_6 = 0.576 = 5.76\%$$

since in MACRS, the salvage value is zero.

INVESTMENT TAX CREDIT

The investment tax credit is only applicable to certain specialized items such as rehabilitation and energy property. However, the inclusion of the 1981 and 1985 investment tax in the text is considered desirable because it may reappear (or something similar).

PROBLEMS_____

S4-1. Determine the taxes and actual tax rates for the following taxable incomes: (a) $500,000, (b) $300,000, (c)$50,000,000, (d) $60,000, and (e) $16,000,000.

S4-2. A company's taxable income is well above \$18,333,333. It has a Sec. 1245 asset that originally cost $\$1.5(10)^6$ and now has a tax book value of $0.3(10)^6$. What are the tax consequences if the asset is sold for (a) $\$0.7(10)^6$, (b) $\$0.1(10)^6$, and (c) $\$2.0(10)^6$.

S4-3. An asset was purchased eight years ago and MACRS (5 years) was used to depreciate the asset for tax purposes. If this asset is sold now for \$20,000, what are the tax consequences using a tax rate of 35%?

S4-4. If an asset costs \$150,000, what is its book value at the end of three years using MACRS (7 years)?

S4-5. Determine the depreciation schedule for an asset that costs \$100,000 with a salvage of \$10,000 using MACRS (5 years).

S4-6. Derive the depreciation percentages for MACRS (7 years).

S4-7. A company has bought an asset for \$200,000 that qualifies for the 1985 investment tax credit (see the text) and MACRS (7 years). Determine the following:

(a) the investment tax credit if the company adjusts the asset's basis for tax depreciation purposes. Also, determine the depreciation for the first year.

(b) repeat Part (a) only the company does not adjust the asset's basis.

CHAPTER 5

THE ECONOMIC EVALUATION
OF A SINGLE PROJECT

This chapter expands the discussion in the text of (1) payout (payback) period and (2) cash flows with decreases in working capital.

PAYOUT PERIOD

In the text, the payout period is defined by Eq. (S5-1)

$$0 = \sum_{j=0}^{P} X_j \qquad (S5\text{-}1)$$

and is based on a discount (MARR) rate of zero. It does mention the possibility of another definition. This other definition is given by Eq. (S5-2)

$$0 = \sum_{j=0}^{P} X_j (P/F\ k,\ j) \qquad (S5\text{-}2)$$

where k is the minimum attractive rate of return (MARR).

EXAMPLE S5-1_____

Using the cash flows in Table S5-1, determine the payout period using (a) MARR = 0 and (b) MARR = 12%.

- - - - - - - - - - - - - - - - - -

Table S5-1 Here

- - - - - - - - - - - - - - - - - -

For Part (a), the sum of the cash flows for four years is

$$-70{,}000 - 100{,}000 + 50{,}000 + 50{,}000 + 50{,}000 = -20{,}000$$

TABLE S5-1

CASH FLOWS FOR EXAMPLE S5-1

EOY	C.F.
0	-70,000
1	-100,000
2	50,000
3	50,000
4	50,000
5	60,000
6	60,000
7	60,000
8	60,000
9	60,000
10	60,000

and for five years is

$$-70,000 - 100,000 + 50,000 + 50,000 + 50,000 + 60,000 = 40,000$$

Therefore, the payout period is between four and five years and using linear interpolation the payout period is

$$p = + \frac{20,000}{60,000} = 4.33 \text{ years.}$$

For Part (b), the discounted cash flows for five years is

$$-70,000 - 100,000 \ P/F \ 12,1 + 50,000 \ PA12,3 \ (P/F \ 12,1)$$

$$+ 60,000 \ P/F \ 12,5 = -18,018$$

and for six years is

$$-1,018 + 60,000 \ P/F \ 12,6 = 12,378$$

Therefore the payout period is

$$p = 5 + \frac{18,018}{30,396} = 5.59 \text{ years.}$$

Decreases in Working Capital

In the text the determination of cash flows for projects that require increases in working capital is presented in detail. However for projects that involve decreases in working capital, a specific numerical example is not provided. Therefore, it is the purpose of this section to provide a numerical example that shows how decreases in working capital are included in cash flows.

Example S5-2. The data for this example is given in Table S5-2. The net equity cash flows using this data are given in Table S5-3 and some sample calculations follow:

See Table S5-2 on next page

- - - - - - - - - - - - - - - - - - -

- - - - - - - - - - - - - - - - - - -

See Table S5-3 on page S5-6

- - - - - - - - - - - - - - - - - - -

$X_0 = -100,000 + .3(100,000) + 10,000 - .3(10,000)$

$= \$\text{-}63,000$

$X_1 = (40,000 - 5,000 - 2,700) - (40,000 - 5,000 - 2,700 - 20,000)(.4)$

$-4,500 + 20,000 - .3(20,000)$

$= \$36,880$

$X_2 = (40,000 - 5,000 - 1,650) - (40,000 - 5,000 - 1,650 - 32,000)(.4)$

$-3,300$

$= \$29,510$

$X_3 = (40,000 - 5,000 - 1,320) - (40,000 - 5,000 - 1,320 - 19,200)(.4)$

$-3,300$

$= \$24,588$

-
-
-

$X_6 = (40,000 - 5,000 - 330) - (40,000 - 5,000 - 3,300 - 5,760)(.4)$

$-3,300 + 16,000 - 30,000$

$= \$5,806$

TABLE S5-2

DATA FOR EXAMPLE S5-2

Capital investment	=	$100,000
Tax depreciation	=	MACRS (5 years)
Project life	=	6 years
Required return on equity	=	25%
Required return on debt	=	10%
Debt ratio	=	30%
Operations and maintenance	=	$5,000 per year
Tax rate	=	40%
Working capital decrease ($j = 0$)	=	$10,000
Working capital decrease ($j = 1$)	=	$20,000
Salvage value	=	$16,000
Gross income	=	$40,000 per year

TABLE S5-3

EQUITY CASH FLOWS FOR EXAMPLE S5-2

EOY	K, L, W	G	C	D	B′	P	I	X
0	$\begin{cases} K = 100{,}000 \\ W = 10{,}000 \end{cases}$	—	—	—	27,000	—	—	-63,000
1	W = 20,000	40,000	5,000	20,000	16,500	4,000	2,700	36,800
2		40,000	5,000	32,000		3,300	1,650	29,510
3		40,000	5,000	19,200		3,300	1,320	24,588
4		40,000	5,000	11,500		3,300	990	21,714
5		40,000	5,000	5,000		3,300	660	21,912
6	L = 16,000	40,000	5,000	5,760		3,300	330	5,806

Now, some of the cash flow calculations need further explanation, particularly, B^1, P, and I values. First in year $j=0$, the term $(0.3)(100,000)$ is the debt portion of the $100,000 total capital expenditure. Since this is borrowed money it is a cash inflow (a positive amount). The $10,000 value is the decrease in working capital and the term $(0.3)(10,000)$ is a debt reduction resulting from the decrease in working capital. Consequently, the net debt requirement is $27,000 (the difference between the $30,000 and $3,000 values). In year two there is another debt reduction of $(0.3)(20,000)$ due to the decrease in working capital of $20,000, meaning a further reduction in debt. This results in an outstanding debt requirement at the end of year one of

$$B^1 = 27,000 - 6,000 - 4,500$$

$$= \$16,500$$

where the $4,500 value is the debt recovery in year one and is based on the condition that the debt is recovered over the life of the project (six years), or

$$P_1 = \frac{27,000}{6} = \$4,500$$

The entire debt recovery and interest is given in Table S5-4. In this table, the P values for years two

- - - - - - - - - - - - - - - - - - - -

Table S5-4 Here

- - - - - - - - - - - - - - - - - - - -

through six are based on recovering the debt over the remaining life of the project (five years), or

$$P_2 \rightarrow P_6 = \frac{16,500}{5} = \$3,300$$

TABLE S5-4

DEBT RECOVERY AND INTEREST
SCHEDULE FOR EXAMPLE S5-2

EOY	B	B′	P	I
0	$\begin{Bmatrix} 30{,}000 \\ -3{,}000 \end{Bmatrix}$	27,000	--	--
1	-6,000	16,500	4,500	2,700
2			3,300	1,650
3			3,300	1,320
4			3,300	990
5			3,300	660
6			3,300	330

The interest is 10% of the unpaid debt and for this example is

$$I_1 = 27,000 (.10) = \$2,700$$

$$I_2 = 16,500 (.10) = \$1,650$$

$$I_3 = (16,500 - 3,300)(.10) = \$1,320$$

In the cash flow for year 6, the total working capital reduction ($30,000) is charged to the project (a negative cash flow). In effect, the reduction in working capital has been used to reduce the projects debt and equity requirements. Consequently, the total amount must be charged to the project. The usual convention is to include this reduction in the year the gross income stops. This is consistent with the convention used in case of increased working capital (see p. 125 of the text).

EXAMPLE S5-3_____

Repeat Example S5-2 only use total cash flows. The solution to this example is less involved than the use of equity cash flows. The total cash flows are given in Table S5-5.

- - - - - - - - - - - - - - - - - - -

Table S5-5 Here

- - - - - - - - - - - - - - - - - - -

Some sample calculations follow:

$$X_0 = -100,000 + 10,000$$

$$= \$-90,000$$

$$X_1 = (40,000 - 5,000) - (40,000 - 5,000 - 20,000)(.4) + 20,000$$

$$= 49,000$$

- •
- •
- •

$$X_6 = (40,000 - 5,000) - (40,000 - 5,000 - 5,760)(.4)$$

$$-30,000 + 16,000$$

$$= \$32,696$$

PROBLEMS

S5-1. Using the cash flows given below, determine the payout period for (a) MARR = 0% and

(b) MARR = 15%.

EOY	C.F.
0	-120,000
1	-100,000
2	80,000
3	100,000
4	100,000
5	120,000
6	120,000
7	120,000
8	120,000

TABLE S5-5

EQUITY CASH FLOWS FOR EXAMPLE S5-2

EOY	K, L, W	G	C	D	X
0	K = 100,000 W = 10,000	—	—	—	-90,000
1	W = 20,000	40,000	5,000	20,000	49,000
2		40,000	5,000	32,000	33,800
3		40,000	5,000	19,200	28,680
4		40,000	5,000	11,500	25,608
5		40,000	5,000	11,520	25,608
6	L = 16,000	40,000	5,000	5,760	32,696

S5-2. Using the data given below, determine the following: (a) net equity cash flows and (b) net total cash flows.

Capital investment (j=0)	= $100,000
Salvage value	= $50,000
Tax depreciation	SL
life, years	10
salvage	$50,000
Gross income per year 10 years	= $300,000
Debt ratio	= 30%
Tax rate	= 40%

Debt is recovered over a ten-year period
on the basis of a constant yearly amount
of the borrowed amount.

S5-3. Repeat Problem S5-2 with a working capital increase in year one of $90,000. Assume any debt portion of the working capital is recovered over the remaining life of the project (9 years).

S5-4. Repeat Problem S5-3 only the working capital ($90,000) is a decrease.

CHAPTER 6

MINIMUM ANNUAL REVENUE REQUIRMENTS

This supplement chapter provides some additional insights into the meaning and implications of minimum annual revenue requirements (R_j). The R_j values could be considered as a basis for establishing a minimum unit selling price (S_j). For if the yearly volume of sales is estimated, the minimum unit selling price could be based on Eq. (S6-1).

$$S_j = \frac{R_j}{V_j} \tag{S6-1}$$

Since, all costs are included in the R_j values plus a yearly profit (F_e) and the recovery of the capital (D_b).

Revenue requirements also show, explicitly, that private companies do expect to recover all invested capital as well as any taxes. For a company, taxes are a cost of doing business and must be recovered. Therefore, the taxes and invested capital are passed on to the consumer by including them in the unit selling price.

DIFFERENT DEBT RECOVERY

It is pointed out in Chapter 6 of the text that the recovery of the debt is over the length of the project. It is accomplished through the book depreciation and salvage values in proportion to the debt ratio (see Eq. (6-2) in the text). It is often asked if other debt recovery schemes can be incorporated into revenue requirements. The answer is, yes. However, it becomes more involved. A different debt recovery method is provided in Example S6-1.

EXAMPLE S6-1_____

     In this example the data given in Table S6-1 is used to generate the revenue requirements

- - - - - - - - - - - - - - - - - - -

Table S6-1 Here

- - - - - - - - - - - - - - - - - - -

in two ways. First, the revenue requirements in Table S6-2 have been generated using the

- - - - - - - - - - - - - - - - - - -

Table S6-2 Here

- - - - - - - - - - - - - - - - - - -

method given in Chapter 6 of the text. This method recovers the debt capital ($42,000) through

the book depreciation as shown in Table S6-3, which uses Eq. (6-2) in the text. In Table S6-4,

the revenue

- - - - - - - - - - - - - - - - - - -

Table S6-3 Here

- - - - - - - - - - - - - - - - - - -

- - - - - - - - - - - - - - - - - - -

Table S6-4 Here

- - - - - - - - - - - - - - - - - - -

requirement for the data in Table S6-1 are given using a different debt recovery method from that

used in Table S6-3. The debt recovery in Table S6-4 is based on the condition that debt is

recovered over four years in equal annual amounts. Some sample calculations follow:

$$\text{debt capital} = K_d = .3(140,000) = \$42,000$$

$$\text{debt recovery} = P_d = \frac{42,000}{4} = \$10,500$$

$$\text{equity capital} = K_e = .7(140,000) = \$98,000$$

TABLE S6-1

DATA FOR EXAMPLE S6-1

Initital investment	=	$140,000
salvage	=	$0
book depreciation	=	straight-line
life	=	7 years
Tax deprciation	=	SYD
life	=	7 years
salvage	=	$0
Annual costs	=	$8,000
Debt ratio	=	30%
Required equity return	=	20%
Required debt return	=	10%
Tax rate	=	40%

TABLE S6-2

REVENUE REQUIREMENT RECOVERY
WITH DEBT RECOVERY IN YEARS 1-7

EOY	D_b	D	K	F_e	I	t	C	R
0	---	---	140,000	---	---	---	---	---
1	20,000	35,000	120,000	19,600	4,200	3,067	8,000	54,867
2	20,000	30,000	100,000	16,800	3,600	4,533	8,000	52,933
3	20,000	25,000	80,000	14,000	3,000	6,000	8,000	51,000
4	20,000	20,000	60,000	11,200	2,400	7,467	8,000	49,067
5	20,000	15,000	40,000	8,400	1,800	8,933	8,000	47,133
6	20,000	10,000	20,000	5,600	1,200	10,400	8,000	45,200
7	20,000	5,000	0	2,800	600	11,867	8,000	43,267

TABLE S6-3

DEBT RECOVERY SCHEDULE
FOR TABLE S6-1

EOY	DEBT RECOVERY
0	---
1	$20,000(.3) = 6,000$
2	$20,000(.3) = 6,000$
3	$20,000(.3) = 6,000$
4	$20,000(.3) = 6,000$
5	$20,000(.3) = 6,000$
6	$20,000(.3) = 6,000$
7	$20,000(.3) + (0)*(.3) = 6,000$

*If the salvage is other than zero, it would occur at

this point (see Eq. (6-2) in the text)

TABLE S6-4

**REVENUE REQUIREMENTS
WITH DEBT RECOVERY IN YEARS 1-4**

EOY	P_b	K_d	P_e	K_e	D_b	D	F_e	I	t	C	R
0		42,000	---	98,000	---	---	---	---	---	---	---
1	10,500	31,500	14,000	84,000	24,500	35,000	19,600	4,200	6,067	8,000	62,367
2	10,500	21,000	14,000	70,000	24,500	30,000	16,800	3,150	7,533	8,000	59,983
3	10,500	10,500	14,000	56,000	24,500	25,000	14,000	2,100	9,000	8,000	57,600
4	10,500	0	14,000	42,000	24,500	20,000	11,200	1,050	10,467	8,000	55,217
5	0	0	14,000	28,000	14,000	15,000	8,400	0	4,933	8,000	35,333
6	0	0	14,000	14,000	14,000	10,000	5,600	0	6,400	8,000	34,000
7	0	0	14,000	0	14,000	5,000	2.800	0	7,867	8,000	32,667

$$\text{equity recovery} = \frac{98,000}{7} = \$14,000$$

total capital recovery = D_b = 10,500 + 14,500 = 24,500

for years one through four and for

five through seven is $14,000

$$\text{tax depreciation} = D_j \; \frac{(n-j+1)(P-L)}{\dfrac{n(n+1)}{2}}$$

$$D_1 = \frac{7}{28}(140,000) = 35,000$$

return on equity = $Fe_j = k_eK_{e,\,j-1}$

$$Fe_1 = (.20)(98,000) = \$19,600$$

$$Fe_2 = (.20)(84,000) = \$16,800$$

return on debt $= I_j = k_dK_{d,\,j-1}$

$$I_1 = (.10)(42,000) = \$4,200$$

$$I_2 = (.10)(31,500) = \$3,150$$

$$\text{taxes} = t_j = (D_b + F_e - D)_j\left(\frac{T}{1-T}\right)$$

$$t_1 = (24,500 + 19,600 - 35,000)\left(\frac{.4}{.6}\right)$$

$$= \$6,067$$

$$t_2 = (24,500 + 16,800 - 30,000)\left(\frac{.4}{.6}\right)$$

$$= \$7,533$$

$$\text{cost} = C = \$8,000 \text{ per year}$$

$$\text{revenue requirements} = R_j = (D_b + F_e + I + t + C)_j$$

$$R_1 = \$24,500 + 19,600 - 4,200$$

$$+ 6,067 + 8,000 = \$62,367$$

$$R_2 = 24,500 + 16,800 + 3,150$$

$$+ 7,533 + 8,000 = \$59,983$$

It should be noted that the equations for F_e and I are different from those used in Chapter 6 of the text. Also, it is pointed out that with a different debt recovery scheme, the total salvage is an equity cash flow. That is, Eq. (6-2) in the text is not used (or implied). A comparison of Tables 6-2 and 6-4 shows that the revenue requirements in Table 6-2 are lower than in Table 6-4 for the early years and are higher for later years. This would result in the NPV being higher, using the revenue requirements in Table 6-2, than the NPV using the revenue requirements in Table 6-4. Using Eq. (6-13) from the text and a gross income (G_j) of $70,000 per year, the NPV of the equity cash flows using the R_j values in Table S6-2 is

$$NPV = (1-.4)\{(70,000 - 54,867)(P/F\ 20,1) + (70,000 - 52,933)\ PF\ 20,2$$

$$+ \ldots + (70,000 - 43,267)\ PF\ 20,7\} = \$42,427$$

and using the R_j values in Table S6-4, the NPV is

$$NPV = (1-.4)\{(70,000 - 62,367)\ P/F\ 20,1 + (70,000 - 59,983)\ PF\ 20,2$$

$$+ \ldots + (70,000 - 32,667)\ PF\ 20,7\} = \$38,420$$

This result, of course, is not surprising. Since, the equity rate of return also varies with the debt recovery method.

PROBLEMS

S6-1. Using the following data, determine the minimum annual revenue requirements

Capital investment	=	$200,000
Salvage	=	$20,000
Life	=	5 years
Tax depreciation	=	SYD
life	=	5 years
salvage	=	$20,000
Operations and Maintenance	=	$40,000 per year
Debt ratio	=	40%
Tax rate	=	40%
Required return for equity	=	25%
Required return for debt	=	12%

S6-2. Repeat Problem S6-2 with the debt being recovered in the first two years on the basis of equal annual amounts of the debt.

S6-3. Repeat Problem 6-1 with a debt ratio of zero.

S6-4. Calculate the NPV of Problems 6-1, 6-2, and 6-3 on the basis of equity cash flows (MARR = 25%) and the gross income is $170,000 per year.

S6-5. From your solutions to Problem 6-1 through 6-4, are any generalizations possible regarding debt financing?

CHAPTER 7

CAPITAL BUDGETING

No additional concepts are presented in this supplement for the text's Chapter 7.

However, there are some interesting implications (ramifications) included in the Problems.

For example, some solutions involve projects with equal NPV and the comparison of

decision criteria.

PROBLEMS_____

S7-1　For the five projects given below, determine the following if MARR = 25%.

　　(a)　which project should be selected if they are mutually exclusive.

　　(b)　which projects should be selected if they are independent.

　　(c)　which projects should be selected with budget restrictions of $300,000, $400,000,

　　　　and $340,000.

	1	2	3	4	5
Capital investment, $	100,000	120,000	150,000	200,000	220,000
Annual cash flow, $	25,000	35,000	45,000	55,000	65,000
Years	10	10	10	10	10

S7-2.　Given below are the capital expenditures (K) and cash flows (CF) for five projects. Note

　　　in year one, the cash flow and capital expenditure have not been combined. For example,

　　　the combined (net) cash flow for project one in year one is –100,000 + 80,000 = -20,000.

If MARR = 20%, determine:

(a)   the project that should be selected if they are mutually exclusive.

(b)   the projects that should be selected if there is no budget restriction.

(c)   the projects that should be selected if the budget for j = 0 is $800,000 and

for j = 1 is $550,000.

S7-3.   Considering the solutions to Problems S7-1 and S7-2, what are the implications

(ramifications) of budget restrictions? Hint: consider the answers to Parts (b) and (c) in

these problems.

S7-4.   For the four projects given below, determine

(a)   the rate of return for each project

(b)   the net present value for each project with MARR = 15%

(c)   the payout period for each project with MARR = 0%

(d)   the B/C ratio for each project using the capital investment as the denominator and

the present value of the positive cash flows (MARR = 15%) as the numerator.

	Project			
	1	2	3	4
Capital investment, $	63,000	90,000	100,000	140,000
Annual cash flow, $	14,000	20,000	25,000	35,000
Years	10	10	10	10

S7-5. Considering your results in Problem S7-4, answer the following questions:

(a)   which project should be selected if they are mutually exclusive? Why?

(b)   considering just Projects 1 and 2, which one should be selected if they are

mutually exclusive?

(c)   same as Part (b) only consider just Projects 3 and 4.

(d)   in considering just Projects 1 and 2, does the B/C ratio or payout period give any

insights which project to select?

(e)   same as Part (d) only for Projects 3 and 4.

(f)   can any generalization be made regarding NPV, rate of return, payout period, and

B/C ratio as project selection criteria?

S7-6. Considering the three mutually exclusive projects given below, determine the following:

(a)   which project should be selected using the incremental rate of return (MARR = 20%)?

(b)   which project should be selected using the NPV (MARR = 20%)?

	Project		
	1	2	3
Capital investment, $	$1(10)^6$	$1.4(10)^6$	$2.0(10)^6$
Cash flow, $	220,000	300,000	420,000
Years	∞	∞	∞

CHAPTER 8

BREAK-EVEN MODELS

This supplement chapter elaborates on some of the equations in Chapter 8 of the text. In addition, a multi-product breakeven model is included. To some, the conversion of Eq. (8-1) to Eq. (8-4) is not readily apparent. Therefore, this conversion is shown in the following presentation. First, Eq. (8-1) in the text is

$$P = (sV - cV - F - D_b - I) - (sV - cV - F - D - I)J \qquad (S8\text{-}1)$$

Now, the overall fixed cost, F^1, is

$$F^1 = F + D_b + I \qquad (S8\text{-}2)$$

and

$$F^1 - D_b = F + I \qquad (S8\text{-}3)$$

Substituting Eq. (S8-2) into the first term of Eq. (S8-2) and Eq. (8-3) into the tax term (second term) of Eq. (S8-1) gives

$$P = (sV - cV - F^1) - (sV - cV - F^1 + D_b - D)T \qquad (S8\text{-}4)$$

$$P = (sV - cV - F^1)(1\text{-}T) - D_bT + DT \qquad (S8\text{-}5)$$

and rearranging gives

$$P = (sV - cV - F^1)(1\text{-}T) + (D - D_b)T \qquad (S8\text{-}5)$$

which is Eq. (8-4) in the text.

The breakeven point with taxes for the case of $D_b = D$ is given in the text as

$$V_b = \frac{F + D_b + I}{s - c} \qquad (S8\text{-}6)$$

which could be expressed as

$$V_b = \frac{F^1}{s - c} \qquad (S8\text{-}7)$$

However, no explicit formula is given for the case $D_b \neq D$. Therefore, it is the purpose of this section to present such a formula. First, expanding Eq. (S8-5) gives

$$P = sV - cV - F^1 + sVT - cVT + F^1T + DT - D_bT \qquad (S8-8)$$

At the breakeven point $P = 0$ and Eq. (S8-9) can be arranged to give

$$F^1 - F^1T - DT + D_bT = sV - cV - sVT + cVT \qquad (S8-9)$$

or

$$F^1(1\text{-}T) - T(D\text{-}D_b) = V(1\text{-}T)(s\text{-}c) \qquad (S8\text{-}10)$$

which gives the breakeven volume, V_b, as

$$V_b = \frac{F^1(1-T) - T(D-D_b)}{(1-T)(s-c)} \qquad (S8\text{-}11)$$

EXAMPLE S8-1 _____

Using the data given below, determine the following:

(a)   the breakeven volume

(b)   the profit with the breakeven volume.

F = fixed expenses without D_b and I = $\$9(10)^6$

I = debt interest   = $\$1(10)^6$

D_b = book (company) depreciation   = $\$4(10)^6$

D = tax depreciation   = $\$4.75(10)^6$

s = unit selling price $\$500$

c = unit costs $\$350$

For Part (a) substituting this data in Eq. (S8-12) gives

$$V_b = \frac{14(10)^6(1-.4) - (.4)(4.75-4.00)(10)^6}{(1-.4)(500-350)}$$

$$= 90,000 \text{ units}$$

For Part b, Eq. (S8-1) is used and gives

$$P = \left[500(90,000) - 350(90,000) - 9(10)^6 - 4(10)^6 - 1(10)^6\right]$$

$$- \left[500(90,000) - 350(90,000) - 9(10)^6 - 4.75(10)^6 - 1(10)^6\right](.4)$$

$$= \left[-.5(10)^6\right] - \left[-1.25(10)^6\right](.4)$$

$$= 0.$$

Part (b) in Example S8-1 needs some explanation. The first term (the before tax term) gives a value of -$.5(10)^6$ which suggests a loss while the tax term gives a +$.5(10)^6$ with the net effect of a zero profit. What is being assumed is, the excess depreciation of

$$(4.75 - 4.00)(10)^6 = .75(10)^6$$

can be used to offset taxes from other operations in the company.

MULTIPRODUCT ANALYSIS

The discussion of break-even models in the text is limited to one product. However, there is, often, more than one product. this multiproduct case can be analyzed, as in the single product case, both analytically and graphically. these methods are shown in the next example.

EXAMPLE S8-1_____

A company is making three products. The cost and sales data are given in Table S8-1. It

- - - - - - - - - - - - - - - - - - -

Table S8-1 Here

- - - - - - - - - - - - - - - - - - -

is required to determine the breakeven point for these products using both an analytical and graphical method.

TABLE S8-1

DATA FOR EXAMPLE S8-1

	Product		
	1	2	3
Selling price per unit	30	60	50
Variable cost per unit	10	30	40
Fixed costs per year	120,000	150,000	140,000
Volume of sales per year	9,000	7,000	16,000

The first step for an analytical solutions is to determine the values in Table S8-2. These values,

- - - - - - - - - - - - - - - - - - -

Table S8-2 Here

- - - - - - - - - - - - - - - - - - -

for product one, are determined in the following manner.

total sales revenue = 30(9,000) + 60(7,000) + 50(16,000

$$= \$1,490,000/year$$

percent of sales $= \dfrac{30(9,000)}{1,490,000} = .1812 = 18.12\%$

percent contribution $= \dfrac{30-10}{30} = .6667 = 66.67\%$

percent contribution per sales = (.1812)(.6667) = .1208 = 12.08%

The other values in Table S8-2 are determined in a similar manner.

The breakeven point, B, is obtained from Eq. (S8-1)

$$B = \frac{F}{a} \tag{S8-1}$$

were

F = sum of fixed costs

a = sum of percent contributions per sales

and for this example is

$$B = \frac{410,000}{.3692} = \$1,110,509/year$$

The yearly profit, P, can be determined from Eq. (S8-2)

$$P = (a)(G)(c) \tag{S8-2}$$

TABLE S8-2

PERCENT SALES AND CONTRIBUTIONS

FOR EXAMPLE S8-1

Product	Percent of Sales	Percent Contribution	Percent Contribution per Sales
1	18.12	66.67	12.08
2	28.19	50.00	14.10
3	53.69	20.00	10.74
Σ			36.92

where

$$G = \text{plant capacity expressed as total sales}$$

$$c = \text{percent capacity expressed as a decimal}$$

Assuming $1,490,000 represents full capacity, the profit for this example is

$$P = (.3692)(1,490,000)(1) - 410,000$$

$$= \$140,108/\text{yar}$$

If the plant is operating at 70% capacity, the profit is

$$P = (.3692)(1,490,000)(.7) - 410,000$$

$$= -\$24,924/\text{year}$$

which indicates a loss.

It is noted that this analysis assumes the product mix (proportions) remain fixed. With this assumption, it is possible to determine the volumes of sales for each product in order to breakeven. Since the volumes are fixed, Eq. (S8-3) is true.

$$\frac{s_i - V_i}{s_i}\left(\frac{s_i V_i}{G}\right) = \frac{s_i - V_i}{s_i}\left(\frac{s_i - V_i}{B}\right) \tag{S8-3}$$

where

s_i = unit selling price for product i

V = unit variable cost for product i

V_{bi} = breakeven volume for product i

G and B have been defined earlier

Solving for V_{bi} gives

$$V_{bi} = \frac{V_i B}{G} \tag{S8-4}$$

and the breakeven volumes for this example are

$$V_{b1} = \frac{9,000(1,110,509)}{1,490,000} = 6,708 \text{ units}/\text{year}$$

$$V_{b2} = \frac{7,000(1,110,509)}{1,490,000} = 5,217 \text{ units}/\text{year}$$

$$V_{b3} = \frac{16,000(1,110,509)}{1,490,000} = 11,925 \text{ units}/\text{year}$$

As a check, the total profit with these breakeven volumes should be zero.

$$P = (6,708)(30\text{-}10) + (5,217)(60\text{-}30) + (11,925)(50\text{-}40) - 410,000$$

$$= -80$$

This result (-80) is due to round-off errors.

The graphical solution for this example is shown in Figure S8-1. this graph is

- - - - - - - - - - - - - - - - - - - -

Figure S8-1 Here

- - - - - - - - - - - - - - - - - - - -

constructed by plotting the cumulative total of sales income as the abscissa and profit or loss as

the ordinate.

First, identify the points of cumulative gross income of the abscissa. These values

(270,000, 690,000, and 1,490,000) are shown in the figure. Next, the fixed cost (a loss) for

product one (-120,000) is located on the ordinate at the zero point on the abscissa. Adding to this

fixed cost the amount $-120,000 + (30\text{-}10)(9,000) = \$60,000$ is plotted on the abscissa point of

270,000. Then adding the fixed cost of product two to the 60,000 amount gives -$90,000. The

remaining calculations are shown in the figure. The end point ($140,000) is joined with the total

fixed costs ($410,000) to give the breakeven point which occurs at the intersection of this line

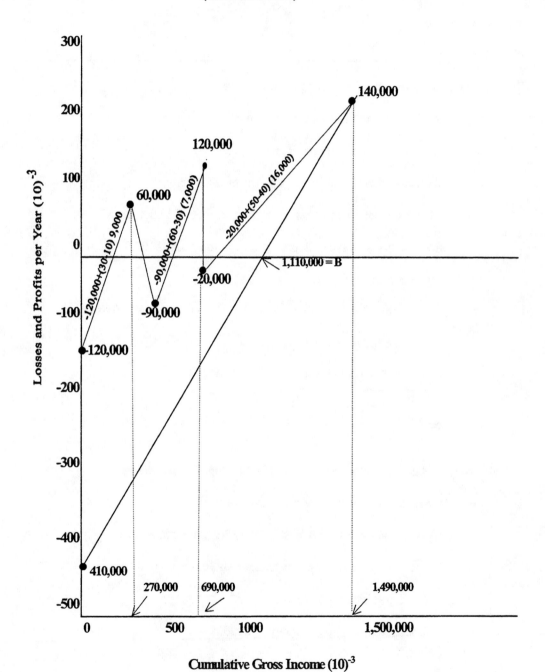

FIGURE S8-1
MULTIPRODUCT BREAKEVEN CHART
(EXAMPLE S8-1)

and the zero profit line. This value is $1,110,000 which is in close agreement with the analytical

solution. The graph also gives the total profit ($140,000) which is in close agreement with the

analytical solution.

PROBLEMS_____

S8-1. For single product with following data, determine:

    (a)   break-even point in terms of volume

    (b)   break-even point in terms of gross sales

    (c)   show that at the break-even point the profit is zero

    (d)   what is the before and after tax profit for sales of 30,000 units

            fixed costs exclusive of depreciation and interest is $300,000

            per year, also

interest	=	$110,000/year
tax and book depreciation	=	$100,000/year
selling price per unit	=	$35
variable cost per unit	=	$10
tax rate	=	40%

S8-2. Using the data in Problem S8-1 with the following changes, determine:

    (a)   the break-even point in terms of volume

    (b)   show that at the break-even point the after-tax profit is zero

    (c)   the before and after tax profit for sales of 30,000 units

    Changes: tax depreciation = $175,000

            book (company) depreciation = $100,000

S8-3. Repeat Problem S8-2 with tax depreciation = $100,000

and book depreciation = $175,000/

S8-4. Using the data given below, and an analytical approach, determine:

(a)   the break-even point

(b)   sales volumes for each product at the break-even point

(c)   the before-tax profit at 100% and 80% capacity, assuming the volumes given represent

100% capacity.

Product	Selling Price	Variable Cost	Volume/ Year	Fixed Costs/ Year
A	50	28	40,000	400,000
B	20	11	70,000	300,000
C	30	16	60,000	500,000
D	60	35	30,000	500,000

S8-5.   Solve for Parts (a) and (c) in Problem S8-4 using the graphical method.

CHAPTER 9

COST COMPARISONS

This supplement chapter provides additional problems that augment the cash flow problems given in the text. There is a statement in the text (p.238, Example 9-5) that, perhaps, needs some additional discussion. This statement involves tax effects at the end of cycles in light of tax rulings regarding "like-kind exchanges." It suggests that tax effects at the end of cycles might not be appropriate where there is cycling of the cost data because this might be considered, from a tax standpoint, a "like-kind exchange." It does suggest that in cases of finite service, the tax effects are appropriate in the last year. A finite need implies that after the service life, there is no need for service. Implying, the asset is eliminated (sold or scraped). When tax effects are included in the text's problems and examples, they are included at the end of each cycle. This is also true for the problems in this chapter of the supplement. In the final analysis one must make a choice on what is considered applicable. The text and this supplement take the point of view that is always easier to eliminate something when it is understood rather than adding something that is not familiar.

PROBLEMS _____

S9-1. Using equity cash flows make a cost comparison of the two assets shown in the following table for an infinite need with no tax effects and no investment tax credit.

	Asset	
	1	2
Initial Cost	75,000	90,000
life, years	4	8
salvage value	5,000	7,000
Annual cost of maintenance		
and operation	10,000	6,000
Tax depreciation	SYD	SYD
Life	4	4
Salvage	0	0
Tax rate	40%	40%
Return on equity	20	20
Ruler on debt	10	10
Debt ratio	40	40

S9-2. In Problem S9-1, the tax effects and investment tax credit (ITC) are omitted. What

changes to the cash flows and equivalent annual amounts would occur if they were

included? Use the 1981 code for the ITC (see p. 90 of the text).

S9-3. Rework Problem S9-1 using total cash flows.

S9-4. Rework Problem S9-3 with tax effects and the investment tax credit (1981).

S9-5. Rework Problem S9-1 for a need of 4 years. If salvage values are needed use the

following table.

EOY	Salvage values	
	Asset 1	Asset 2
1	55,000	70,000
2	30,000	50,000
3	15,000	30,000
4	5,000	20,000
5	-	10,000
6	-	7,000

S9-6. Include tax effects and investment tax credits (penalties) in Problem S9-5.

S9-7. If the service life is greater than eight years, what changes would occur in the solution Problems S9-1 through S9-6?

S9-8. Using equity cash flows, make a cost comparison of the two assets given below for an infinite service with no tax effects and no investment tax credit.

	Asset	
	1	2
Initial Cost	15,000	200,000
life, years	6	10
salvage value	10,000	20,000
Annual cost of maintenance		
and operation	18,000	10,000
Tax depreciation	MACRS (5 years)	
Tax rate	40%	40%
Return on equity	20	20
Ruler on debt	10	10
Debt ratio	30	30

S9-9. Include the investment tax credit (1981 code) and any tax effects in Problem S9-8.

S9-10. Rework Problem S9-8 using total cash flows.

S9-11. Include the investment tax credit (1981 code) and tax effects in Problem S9-10.

S9-12. Rework Problem S9-8 for a service life (need) of fifteen years. If salvage values are needed use the table below.

EOY	Salvage values	
	Alt. 1	Alt. 2
1	-	-
2	60,000	110,000
3	30,000	80,000
4	20,000	50,000
5	15,000	40,000
6	10,000	30,000
7	-	20,000
8	-	20,000
9	-	20,000
10	-	20,000

S9-13. Rework problem S9-12 including tax effects and investment tax credits or penalties.

CHAPTER 10

REPLACEMENT ANALYSIS

This supplement chapter provides additional cash flow replacement problems to augment the problems in the text.

PROBLEMS _____

S10-1. Five years ago, an asset with the data shown below was purchased and put in service. Because this existing asset's operation and maintenance and operation costs have been high, a replacement is being considered. This existing asset, at present, is worth $90,000. It is estimated it will last three more years and have a salvage value of $5,000 at that time. It is also estimated that operation and maintenance costs will be 40,000 per year. The data for the replacement asset are shown below:

Original Data for Existing Asset	
Initial Cost	$170,000
life, years	10
salvage value	$5,000
Tax depreciation	SYD
Life, years	10
Salvage	$5,000
Tax rate	30%
Required debt return	12.5%
Required equity return	25%
Tax rate	52%

S10-1 (con't.).

Data for Replacement Asset	
Initial Cost	$170,000
life, years	8
salvage value	$10,000
Annual cost of operation	
and maintenance	$20,000
Tax depreciation	MACRS (5 years)
Debt ratio	40%
Required debt return	10%
Required equity return	20%
Tax rate	40%

Using an infinite service life and equity cash flows make a cost comparison assuming no investment tax or tax effects.

S10-2. Repeat Problem S10-1 including the investment tax (1981 Code) and tax effect considerations.

S10-3. Repeat problem S10-1 for a service life of seven years. If salvage values are needed for the new asset, use the table given below:

EOY	Salvage Values
1	100,000
2	70,000
3	40,000
4	30,000
5	20,000
6	15,000
7	12,000
8	10,000

S10-4.   Repeat Problem S10-3 including investment tax and tax effect considerations.

S10-5.   Repeat Problem S10-2 using total cash flows.

S10-6.   It has been determined that is possible to overhaul the asset in Problem S10- 1. The overhaul will cost $40,000 and extend the life of the existing asset to five years with a total (old plus overhaul) salvage of $8,000. It has determined that the overhaul cost can be split into $10,000 as an expense and $30,000 as a depreciable asset using MACRS (5 years). It is estimated with the overhaul the annual cost of operation and maintenance is $30,000. Determine the equity cash flows for this overhaul alternative and equivalent annual amount.

S10-7.   Include investment tax (1981 code) and tax effects in Problem S10-6.

S10-8.   Compare the results of Problems S10-1 and S10-6 and determine which is the best alternative.

CHAPTER 11

MINIMUM ANNUAL REVENUE REQUIREMENT EXTENSIONS

This chapter in the text considers the normalizing method for generating revenue requirements and the inclusion of working capital changes in revenue requirements. In this supplement chapter no new information is provided for the normalizing method. However, there is an important point for working capital.

Basically, the debt recovery method used with working capital changes is different in Chapter 11 than in Chapter 5 of the text. The method used in Chapter 5 is based on the equal annual recovery of the debt (borrowed money) with interest assessed on the unrecovered amount. In Chapter 11, the method used is a constant interest amount with the debt recovered in the last year. This difference is particularly important when generating equity cash flows. The difference is shown and discussed in Example S11-1.

Example S11-1 _____

The Chapter 5 method is shown in Table S11-1 for a working capital increase of $40,000,

- - - - - - - - - - - - - - - - - -

Table S11-1 Here

- - - - - - - - - - - - - - - - - -

a debt ratio of 40%, and the debt being recovered over five years with a debt interest rate of 10%. As in Chapter 5, the total working capital is recovered at the end. In Chapter 5, the convention used is to recover the working capital in year the gross income stops. The entire recovery of working capital is an equity return since all the debt ($16,000) has been recovered. As pointed out previously, this is a yearly constant recovery of the debt with interest assessed on the unrecovered amount. The table shows the change in equity cash flows (ΔCF) resulting from the

TABLE S11-1

DEBT RECOVERY METHOD USED IN CHAPTER 5

EOY	W	B	P	I	ΔCF
0	-	-	-	-	0
1.	-40,000	+16,000	-	-	-14,000
2.	-	-	-3,200	-1,600	-4,160
3.	-	-	-3,200	-1,280	-3,968
4.	-	-	-3,200	-960	-3,776
5.	-	-	-3,200	-640	-3,584
6.	-	-	-3,200	-320	+36,608

increase in working capital. If a decrease is involved the signs in Table S11-1 would be reversed. Some sample calculations follow:

$$\Delta CF_0 = 0$$

$$\Delta CF_1 = -40,000 + 16,000 = -14,000$$

$$\Delta CF_2 = -1,600 - (-1,600)(.4) - 3,200 = -4,160$$

$$\Delta CF_3 = -1,280 - (-1,280)(.4) - 3,200 = -3,968$$

- •

- •

- •

$$\Delta CF_6 = -320 - (-320)(.4) = 3,200 + 40,000$$

$$= 36,608$$

Table S11-2 shows the debt recovery system used in Chapter 11 for working capital

- - - - - - - - - - - - - - - - - -

Table S11-2 Here

- - - - - - - - - - - - - - - - - -

changes. The interest is a yearly constant ($1,600) and the entire debt ($16,000) is recovered in the last year from the working capital. The remaining amount ($14,000) is a return to equity. In solving the problems in Chapter 11, the constant interest method should be used for the working changes. Some sample calculations follow:

$$\Delta CF_0 = 0$$

$$\Delta CF_1 = -40,000 + 16,000 = \$-14,000$$

$$\Delta CF_2 = -1,600 - (-1,600)(.4) = \$-960$$

TABLE S11-2

DEBT RECOVERY METHOD USED IN CHAPTER 11

EOY	W	B	P	I	ΔCF
0	-	-	-	-	0
1.	-40,000	+16,000	-	-	-14,000
2.	-	-	-	-1,600	-960
3.	-	-	-	-1,600	-960
4.	-	-	-	-1,600	-960
5.	-	-	-	-1,600	-960
6.	+40,000	-	-	-1,600	+13,040

-
-
-

$$\Delta CF_6 = -1,600 - (-1,600)(.4) + 40,000 - 16,000$$

$$= \$13,040$$

PROBLEMS _____

S11-1. Using the data given below, determine the minimum annual revenue requirements and calculate the net present value for equity cash flows (20%) using the following

Gross income	=	$150,000.
Initial cost	=	SL
Both depreciation	=	8
life, years	=	8
salvage	=	$50,000
Tax depreciation	=	MACRS (5 years)
Debt ratio	=	40%
Cost of debt capital	=	10%
Required equity return	=	20%
Tax rate	=	40%
Operation and maintenance	=	$40,000 per year

S11-2. Using the data in Problem S11-1, determine the equity cash flows using an annual gross income of $150,000. Also, calculate the net present value. Use Eq. (6-2) to determine debt recovery (P) values.

S11-3. Determine the revenue requirements using the data in problem S11-1 and a working capital increase of $30,000 occurring in year one. Also determine the net present value (NPV) using a yearly gross income of $150,000.

S11-4. Include the working capital increase in Problem S11-2 and calculate the NPV. Hint: The answers to this problem and Problem S11-3 should be the same.

S11-5. Rework Problem S11-3 only changing the working capital ($30,000) to a decrease.

S11-6. Rework Problem S11-2 with the working capital ($30,000) as a decrease. Hint: The answers to problems S11-5 and S11-6 should be the same.

CHAPTER 12

THE COST OF CAPITAL AND THE MINIMUM

ATTRACTIVE RATE OF RETURN

The text provided detailed methods for determining the cost of various types of capital as well as an average weighted cost of capital for a company. In order to finance its new investments, a company raises a "pool-of-capital" from a mix of common stock, retained earnings, preferred stock, and various forms of debt. The text makes the statement (p. 351) that the basis of establishing a minimum attractive rate of return (MARR) is the incremental weighted average cost of capital of this pool-of-capital. However, a mathematical basis for this statement is not provided. Therefore, it is the purpose of the next section to provide, mathematically, a basis for this statement.

A BASIS FOR THE EVALUATION OF NEW PROJECTS[1]

A company's current market value is

$$P = S + D \qquad \text{(S12-1)}$$

where

S = current market value of common stock

D = current market value of debt

after a pool-of-capital is raised, the company's new market value, P_1, is

$$P_1 = S_1 + D_1 + M \qquad \text{S12-2)}$$

S_1 = new market value of past common stock

D_1 = new market value of past debt

---

[1] Much of the following derivation is based on a presentation in <u>The Economic Analysis of Industrial Projects</u>, 2nd Ed., by Lynn E. Bussey and Ted G. Eschenbach, Prentice-Hall, 1992, pp. 146-147.

M = the additional money raised by either equity, debt, or a combination of both for capital investments (projects)

In order to accept M, it must not reduce the value of the company's common stock. Therefore,

$$S_1 - S \geq 0 \tag{S12-3}$$

and there is a minimal rate of return, k_m, that satisfies this condition. To determine k_m Eq. (S12-1) is subtracted from Eq. (S12-2) which gives

$$P_1 - P = S_1 + D_1 + M - S - D \tag{S12-4}$$

at this point it is assumed that $D_1 = D$ on the basis that new projects will not change the market value of old bonds (debt). Therefore,

$$P_1 - P - M = S_1 - S \tag{S12-5}$$

and substituting Eq. (S12-3)

$$P_1 - P - M \geq 0 \tag{S12-6}$$

or

$$P_1 - P \geq M \tag{S12-7}$$

The company's market value, P, is

$$P = \frac{Y}{1+k} \tag{S12-8}$$

where

k = the average cost of capital used to capitalize the net cash flow stream

Y = the company's future expected cash flow stream from accepted projects.

If a company invests M dollars in projects whose expected rate of return is k_m, the company's new value is

$$P_1 = \frac{Y + M(1 + k_m)}{1 + k_1} \tag{S12-9}$$

where k_1 is the new average cost of capital.

At this point it is noted that the derivation of Eq. (S12-9) is based on one period of time rather than many periods. This makes the derivation algebraically easier and there is no loss in generality.

Substituting Eqs. (S12-8) and (S12-9) into Eq. (12-7) gives

$$\frac{Y + M(1 + k_m)}{1 + k_1} - \frac{Y}{1 + k} \geq M \tag{S12-10}$$

or

$$\frac{Y}{1 + k}\left(\frac{1 + k}{1 + k_1} - 1\right) + \frac{M(1 + k_m)}{1 + k_1} \geq M \tag{S12-11}$$

Substituting Eq. (S12-8) gives

$$P\left(\frac{1 + k}{1 + k_1} - \right) + \frac{M(1 + k_{m)}}{1 + k_1} \geq M \tag{S12-12}$$

and multiplying by $(1+k_1)$ gives

$$P(1 + k - 1 - k_1) + M(1 + k_m) \geq M(1 + k_1) \tag{S12-13}$$

Finally, solving for k_m gives

$$k_m = k_1 + \frac{P}{M}(k_1 - k) \tag{S12-14}$$

Example S12-1 _____

A company's present capital structure is shown in table S12-1 and totals twenty million

- - - - - - - - - - - - - - - - - - - -

Table S12-1 Here

- - - - - - - - - - - - - - - - - - - -

TABLE S12-1

A COMPANY'S PRESENT CAPITAL STRUCTURE

Source	Amount	Proportion	After tax Cost (%)	Weighted Cost
Bonds	$6(10)^6$	.30	3.6	.0108
Preferred stock	$3(10)^6$	.15	8.0	.0120
Retained earnings	$1(10)^6$	.05	11.0	.0055
Common stock	$\underline{10(10)^6}$	$\underline{.50}$	12.0	$\underline{.0600}$
	$20(10)^6$	1.00		.0883

dollars with a weighted average cost of 0.0883. New projects are to be financed by the capital shown in Table S12-2 with a total of five million dollars and a weighted cost of 0.1022. Combining

----

Table S12-2 Here

----

the data in Tables S12-1 and S12-2 gives Table S12-3. Using Eq. (S12-14) gives

----

Table S12-3 Here

$$k_m = .09108 + \frac{20(10)^6}{5(10)^6}(.09108-.0883)$$

$$= .1022 = 10.22\%$$

which is exactly the incremental value obtained in Table S12-2.

PROBLEMS _____

S12-1. A company's present capital structure and after tax costs of capital are

   debt $= 3(10)^6$ at 5%

   equity $= 7(10)^6$ at 20%

   If the company raises an additional six million for new projects in the same proportions and cost as the present, what is the cost of capital for the new projects?

S12-2. Repeat Problem S12-1 only with the additional six million entirely financed by equity at the same cost as Problem S12-1.

TABLE S12-2

INCREMEMENTAL CAPITAL

Source	Amount	Proportion	After tax Cost (%)	Weighted Cost
Bonds	$2(10)^6$	.40	4.8	.0192
Retained earnings	$.5(10)^6$	.10	13.0	.0130
Common stock	$\underline{2.5(10)^6}$	$\underline{.50}$	14.0	$\underline{.0700}$
	$5.0(10)^6$	1.00		.1022

TABLE S12-3

COMBINED CAPITAL STRUCTURE

Financing Source	Present Amount	Increment	Future Amount	Future Ratio	After Tax Cost	Weighted Cost
Bonds	$6(10)^6$	-	$6(10)^6$	.24	3.6	.00864
Bonds	-	$2(10)^6$	$2(10)^6$	.08	4.8	.00384
Retained earnings	$1(10)^6$	-	$1(10)^6$	.04	11.0	.0044
Retained earnings	-	$.5(10)^6$	$.5(10)^6$	.02	13.0	.0026
Preferred stock	$3(10)^6$	-	$3(10)^6$	.12	8.0	.0096
Common stock	$10(10)^6$	-	$10(10)^6$	.40	12.0	.0480
Common stock	-	$2.5(10)^6$	$2.5(10)^6$	.10	14.0	.0140
	$20(10)^6$	$5(10)^6$	$25(10)^6$	1.00		.09108

S12-3. Repeat Problem S12-1 only with the additional six million entirely financed by debt at the sum cost as Problem S12-1.

S12-4. Repeat Problem S12-1 with the following mix and cost

debt $= 2(10)^6$ at 6%

equity $= 4(10)^6$ at 2%

S12-5. A company has the existing capital structure and after-tax costs shown below:

bonds $= 9(10)^6$ at 6%

mortgages $= 6(10)^6$ at 4%

preferred stock $= 8(10)^6$ at 12%

retained earnings $= 15(10)^6$ at 18%

common stock $= 12(10)^6$ at 20%

It plans to finance a group of projects in the following manner:

bonds $= 4(10)^6$ at 8%

retained earnings $= 2.5(10)^6$ at 14%

common stock $= 3.5(10)^6$ at 22%

Determine the cost of capital for the new projects.